Sentences to Paragraphs

For learning the basic writing skills

Book 2

George Davidson

First published 2005 by **Learners Publishing Pte Ltd**
222 Tagore Lane, #03-01 TG Building, Singapore 787603

Email: learnpub@learners.com.sg
Visit our website: http://www.learners.com.sg

Reprinted 2005, 2006, 2007, 2008, 2009, 2011

ISBN 978 981 4133 66 1

Printed by Seng Lee Press Pte Ltd, Singapore

Contents

Preface

Sentences to Paragraphs is a series of four workbooks designed to provide children aged 7 to 9 with practice in sentence and paragraph construction.

Starting with the simple sentence, the books progress in easy and graded steps through the various types of sentence and their parts, the expansion of sentences by means of adjectives and adverbs, the linking of sentences by means of conjunctions, and the combining of sentences into paragraphs, covering many other important topics on the way.

Each unit consists of two or more pages of explanatory material, with each point carefully illustrated with helpful examples, followed by four or five exercises which afford ample practice of the new material. Answers to the exercises are provided at the back of the book.

Thanks are due to Y H Mew for his help with the preparation of these books.

George Davidson

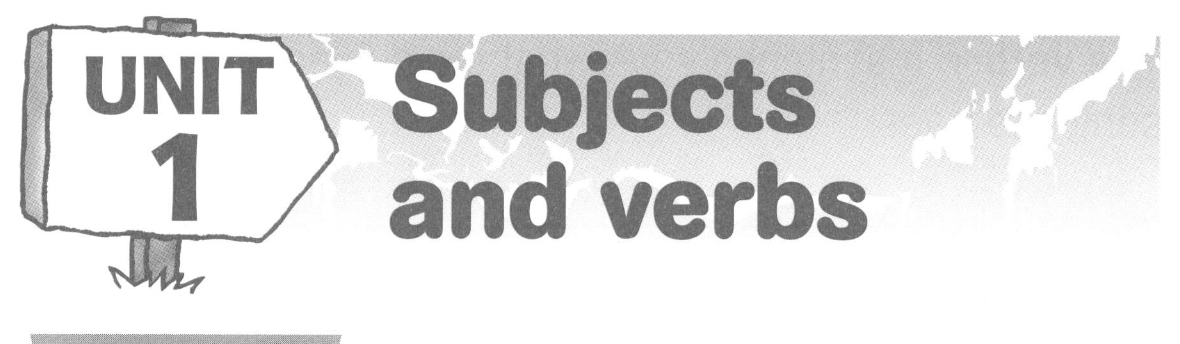

UNIT 1 Subjects and verbs

Lesson

Sentences that are **statements** or **questions** must have a **subject** and a **verb**.

The **subject** of a sentence is the noun or pronoun for the person, animal or thing that does something.

*The **blue** words in these sentences are the **subjects** of the sentences.*

The monkeys are eating bananas.

My balloon has burst.

Mummy is making a cake for my birthday.

The hippopotamus opened its huge mouth.

The **verb** in a sentence says what the subject of the sentence does.

*The **blue** words in these sentences are **verbs**.*

Now I **will put** the cake in the oven.

The baby **is playing** with his toy ducks in the bath.

Jane **can sing** very loudly.

Dinosaurs **lived** a long time ago.

Sometimes a verb does not say what the subject of the sentence does. It just joins the subject to a following word or phrase.

Exercises

A *Draw a circle round the* ***subject*** *of each of the following sentences.*

Handy Tips

In some **questions**, the subject comes **in the middle of the verb**, not in front of it.

1. Who spilt the milk?
2. The pirates buried their treasure under a tree.
3. The teacher blew her whistle.
4. My shoes were hurting my feet.
5. The nurse tied a bandage round George's arm.
6. The ghost moaned quietly.
7. The two boys were quarrelling about something.
8. My dad and I climbed to the top of that hill.
9. Are you going to the gym too?
10. Are Jo and her brother learning to skate?
11. Is the kettle boiling?
12. We are going to the zoo tomorrow.

B *Underline the* ***verb*** *in each of these sentences.*

Handy Tips

In some **questions**, the subject comes in the middle of the verb, so **the verb is in two parts**.

1. I must go now.
2. We will see you later.
3. Lemons are yellow.
4. We found some old coins on the beach.
5. The horses were galloping round the field.
6. The man was wearing an old, dirty coat.
7. How long is that piece of string?
8. Every country has its own special flag.
9. Mum and Dad have bought my brother a puppy.
10. Have you washed your hands?
11. Why are you carrying that bucket?
12. I have found my key.
13. Is John coming to your party?
14. Hasn't he replied to your invitation?

C *Fill in the blanks with words that make suitable subjects for these sentences.*

EXAMPLE:

The sun was shining in the sky.

Handy Tips

A sentence must **make sense.**

1. ______________ were barking loudly.
2. ______________ helped me with my homework.
3. ______________ was reading a newspaper.
4. ______________ is green.
5. Did ______________ answer all the questions?
6. ______________ was blowing through the trees.
7. Are ______________ going to the beach today?
8. Can ______________ help you lay the table?
9. ______________ bought everyone a present.
10. ______________ were playing football.
11. ______________ rode the horse yesterday?
12. ______________ came out of the spaceship?

D *Fill in the blanks with suitable words to complete these sentences.*

EXAMPLE:

The children were

watching television.

Handy Tips

A sentence must **make sense**. Look for clues in the rest of the sentence.

1. The pirates ______________ the treasure on the beach.
2. The chickens were ______________ round the farmyard.
3. We ______________ to the cinema last week.
4. The children were ______________ their lunch.
5. Earthworms ______________ in the ground.
6. The woman was ______________ a basket of flowers.
7. Sheila is ______________ gloves to keep her hands warm.
8. Cats ______________ milk with their tongues.
9. The boys are ______________ a castle out of cardboard.
10. Sugar and honey ______________ sweet.
11. Kangaroos ______________ fast by jumping.
12. The tortoise ______________ slowly along the path.

E *Look at the pictures. Write a suitable sentence for each of them.*

1. ______________________________

2. ______________________________

3. ______________________________

4. ______________________________

5. ______________________________

6. ______________________________

UNIT 2 Commands

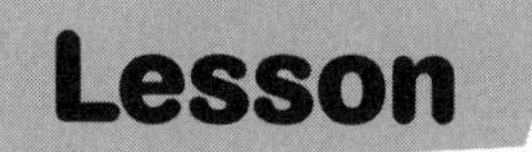

Lesson

A sentence that **tells** you to do something is called a **command**.

A command always has a **verb**. A command usually does not have a **subject**.

Look at these commands. The words in ***blue*** *are verbs.*

Stand beside me.

Don't move.

Wait for me.

Sit down.

Language Help

A command usually has no subject. But sometimes the subject word "you" does appear in a command:

- **You** sit over there.
- **You** stand beside me.

The subject of a command is always "you".

A command usually has a **full stop** at the end.

Here are commands that end with full stops.

If you are making **a very strong command**, you may write an **exclamation mark** (**!**) at the end of it.

Here are strong commands.

Exercises

A *Write **S** in the box if the sentence tells you something. Write **C** in the box if the sentence tells you to do something.*

1. Susie is running to meet her mother.
2. Don't cycle so fast.
3. Robert is going to feed the ducks.
4. Go and feed the ducks.
5. Please don't jump in the puddles.
6. The children were jumping in all the muddy puddles.
7. I left my book on the bus.
8. You have forgotten your book.
9. Don't forget to bring your swimming costume.
10. Don't run across the road.
11. Walk slowly.
12. Watch out for cars.

B *Write out the sentences. Put a* ***full stop*** *at the end of each* ***statement*** *and* ***command****. Put* ***a question mark*** *at the end of each* ***question****.*

1. we are going to write a story about a princess and a dragon

2. write about the princess being shut up in a dungeon

3. what was the princess's name

4. the princess's name was Flora

5. what shall we call the dragon

6. call the dragon George

7. was the princess afraid of George

8. George was a very gentle dragon

C Put the words in each group in the correct order to make a **command**.

Handy Tips

Don't forget to put a **capital letter** at the beginning of each sentence and a **full stop** or **exclamation mark** at the end of the sentence.

1. door the open

2. there this take

3. at pretty those look flowers all

4. be don't noisy please so

5. of draw a a bus picture

6. the football don't in play house

7. with careful be sharp that knife

8. from stay wasps' away nest that

D *Underline the commands in this story.*

The glass slipper

There was once a king. One day, one of his servants found something very surprising. "Show me this surprising thing," said the king. "Bring it to me."

It was a small, glass slipper. "Whose is this slipper?" asked the king. "Go into the town. Search everywhere. Find the owner of the slipper."

The servant went off into the town. He knocked on every door. "Are there any girls in this house?" asked the servant. "Bring them to me." To each girl the servant said, "Try on this slipper." But the girls' feet were always too big.

Finally the servant came to a house where he saw a young girl working in the kitchen. "Put this slipper on," said the king's servant. The girl tried it on. It fitted! The servant had found the right girl at last!

When the king met the girl, he fell in love with her. "Please marry me," he said. The girl happily agreed.

E *Look at these notices. Write out what each says in the form of a command.*

EXAMPLE:

ANSWER: Do not drop litter here.

1. ______________________

2. ______________________

3. ______________________

4. ______________________

5. ______________________

6. ______________________

UNIT 3 Exclamations

Lesson

An **exclamation** is a sentence that **expresses strong feeling** (for example, how you feel when you are very happy or angry or surprised). It begins with a capital letter and ends with an exclamation mark (**!**).

Some exclamations are like statements, but you write an ***exclamation mark*** *instead of a full stop at the end of the sentence.*

*Some exclamations begin with **what** or **how**.*

*Exclamations do not always have a subject and a verb. Here are exclamations that have **no subject or verb**.*

Exercises

A *Put a **question mark** at the end of a **question**. Put an **exclamation mark** at the end of an **exclamation**.*

1. What are you drawing
2. What a lovely picture you've drawn
3. How nice it is to be here
4. How much does an apple cost
5. You're going to fall
6. What a good dog you are
7. You're so good to me
8. What's the matter
9. Someone has taken my bike
10. What a nuisance
11. What has happened
12. How did you hurt your head

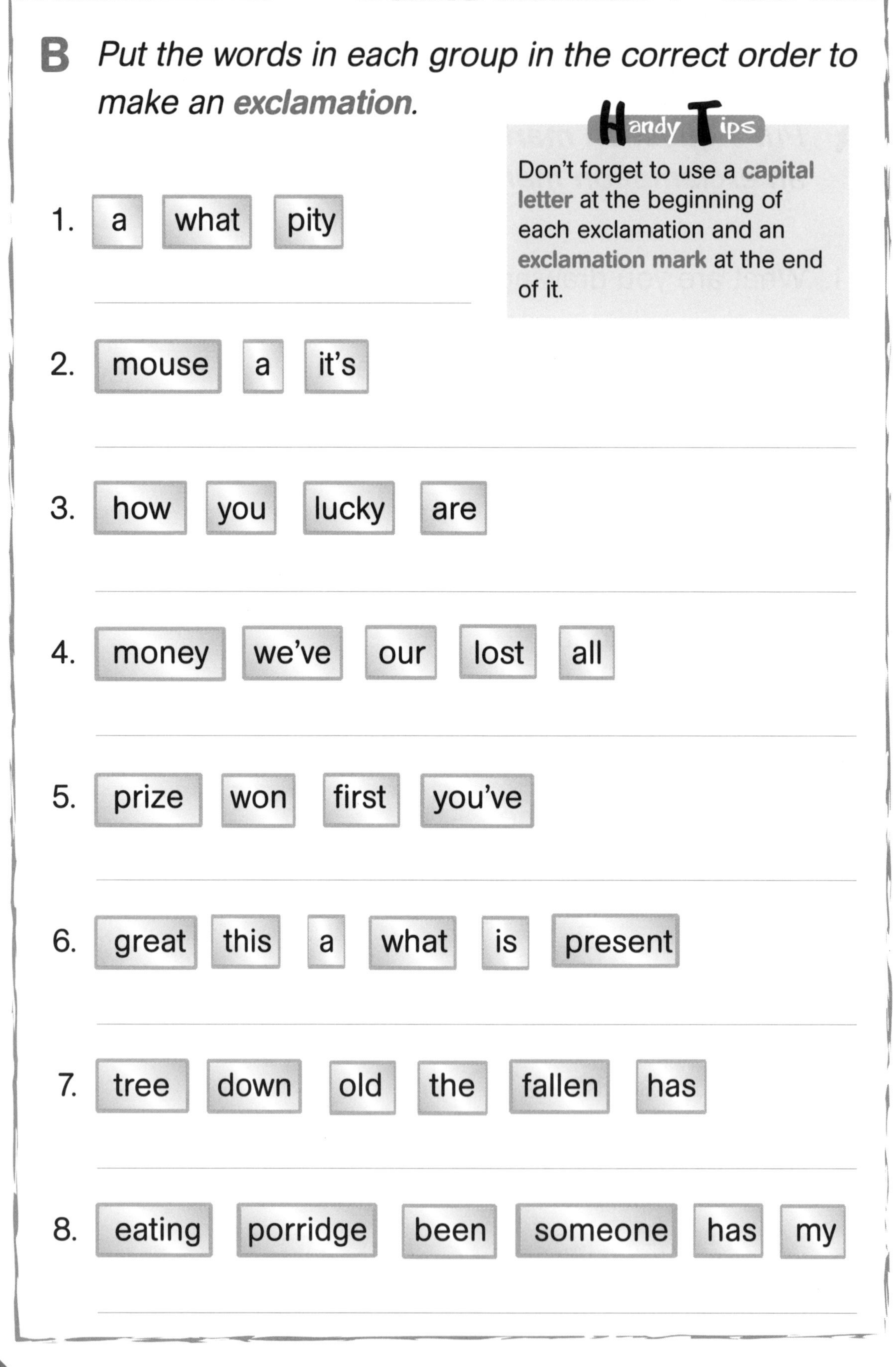

B *Put the words in each group in the correct order to make an* ***exclamation****.*

Handy Tips

Don't forget to use a **capital letter** at the beginning of each exclamation and an **exclamation mark** at the end of it.

1. a | what | pity

2. mouse | a | it's

3. how | you | lucky | are

4. money | we've | our | lost | all

5. prize | won | first | you've

6. great | this | a | what | is | present

7. tree | down | old | the | fallen | has

8. eating | porridge | been | someone | has | my

C *Join each beginning with a suitable ending to make a sentence.*

BEGINNINGS	ENDINGS
1. How lucky	burst my balloon!
2. What a good girl	isn't working!
3. Those bad boys	frightened!
4. That dog	being silly!
5. I've hurt	poor donkey!
6. I'm	we are!
7. The computer	she is!
8. The giant was	my pencil!
9. You're just	bit me!
10. That	tiny spider!
11. He's broken	taller than a tree!
12. What a	my knee!

D *Look at each picture and the sentence beside it. What do you think the same person might say next? Choose a suitable exclamation from the box and write it to complete the speech.*

What a pity!	**How careless of me!**
How lovely!	**What a mess you've made!**
What a surprise!	**How funny he looks!**
What a clever boy!	**What a lucky girl I am!**

1. Are those flowers for me?

____

____

2. Have you missed the bus?

____

____

3. There's paint all over the carpet!

____

____

4. I've got the best Mummy and Daddy in the world!

5. I've broken the clock!

6. I didn't expect to meet you here!

7. Did you paint that picture by yourself?

8. Look at what that man is wearing!

E *Look at each picture. Then write a suitable exclamation in the speech bubble.*

UNIT 4 Objects

Lesson

The **object** in a sentence is the noun or pronoun for the person, animal or thing that receives the action described by the verb.

*The **blue** words in these sentences are the **objects** of the verbs.*

Tom threw **the ball**.

We've spent **all our money.**

The pirates buried **the treasure**.

The boys are building **a raft**.

Now look at these groups of words.

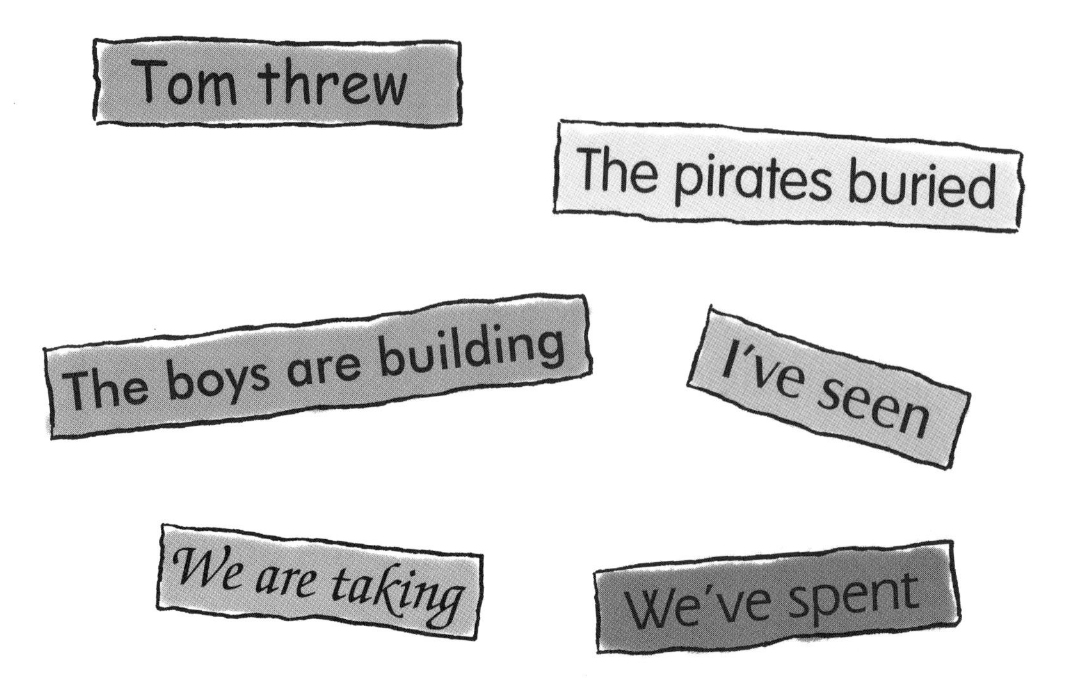

*Can you see that something is missing from each group? The word group does not have an object. Without an object, the word group does not make complete sense. All the word groups are **not sentences.***

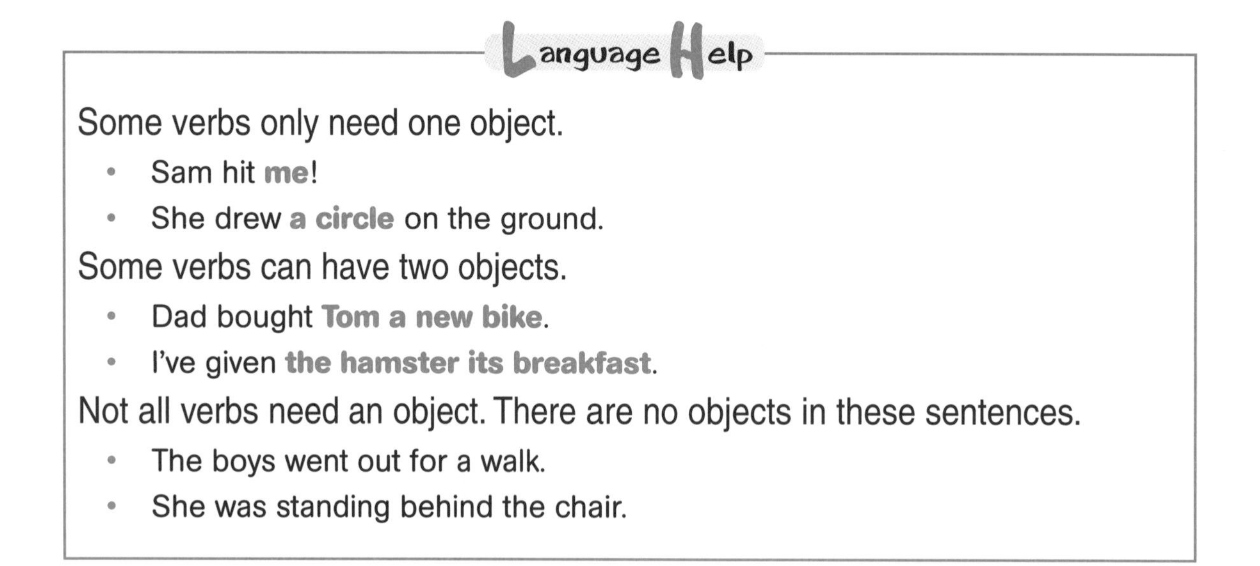

Language Help

Some verbs only need one object.

- Sam hit **me**!
- She drew **a circle** on the ground.

Some verbs can have two objects.

- Dad bought **Tom a new bike**.
- I've given **the hamster its breakfast**.

Not all verbs need an object. There are no objects in these sentences.

- The boys went out for a walk.
- She was standing behind the chair.

Exercises

A *Draw circles round the objects in these sentences.*

Some verbs may have two objects.

1. Tom is feeding the ducks.
2. Paul was eating a sandwich.
3. Grace plays the piano beautifully.
4. Ben and Sarah are blowing soap bubbles.
5. Jean is watching television in her bedroom.
6. Robin lent me his bicycle.
7. Simon is painting a picture of a castle.
8. George is chasing the sheep and lambs.
9. I'm reading a very interesting book.
10. We've got two rabbits and a cat.
11. Mary gave her aunt a bunch of roses.
12. Alice is collecting pebbles on the beach.

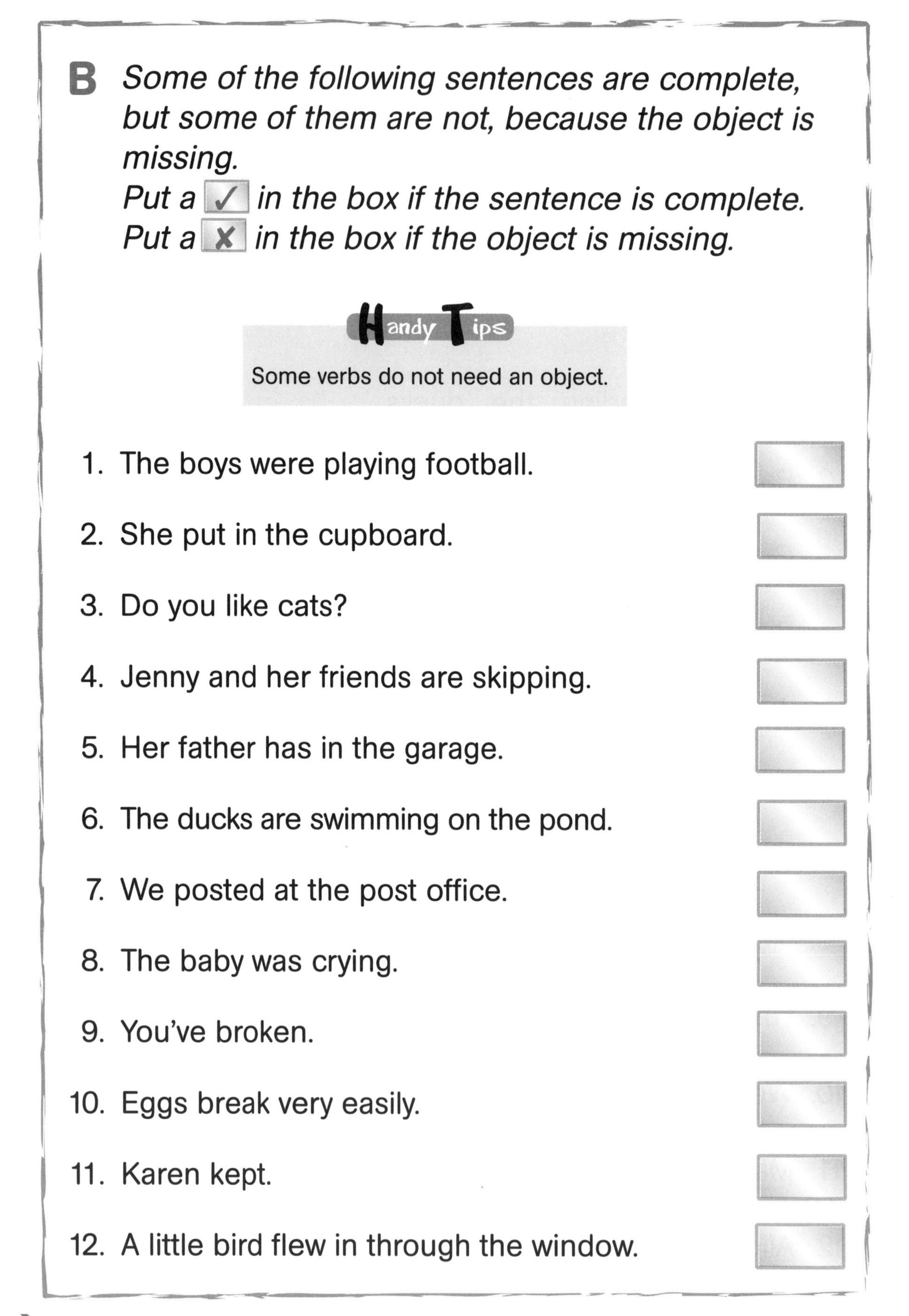

B *Some of the following sentences are complete, but some of them are not, because the object is missing.*
Put a ✓ in the box if the sentence is complete.
Put a ✗ in the box if the object is missing.

Handy Tips

Some verbs do not need an object.

1. The boys were playing football. ☐
2. She put in the cupboard. ☐
3. Do you like cats? ☐
4. Jenny and her friends are skipping. ☐
5. Her father has in the garage. ☐
6. The ducks are swimming on the pond. ☐
7. We posted at the post office. ☐
8. The baby was crying. ☐
9. You've broken. ☐
10. Eggs break very easily. ☐
11. Karen kept. ☐
12. A little bird flew in through the window. ☐

C Complete the following sentences by filling the spaces with suitable objects.

Handy Tips

You can choose any object for each sentence, but the sentence must **make sense**.

1. Martin was eating ____________________.
2. Anne read ____________________ carefully.
3. The cat was watching ____________________ on the grass.
4. Mary is wearing ____________________.
5. Paul put ____________________ in the refrigerator to keep it cold.
6. Sue spread ____________________ on the biscuits.
7. Tom saw ____________________ in the tree.
8. Dick has written ____________________ for the school magazine.
9. Harry's father bought ____________________ for the show.
10. Kate was licking ____________________.
11. Adam likes ____________________.
12. I've finished ____________________.

D *Complete the following sentences by filling the spaces with suitable verbs.*

Handy Tips

You can choose any verb for each sentence, but the sentence must **make sense**.

1. Mary is ______________ flowers in the garden.
2. Billy is ______________ his drum noisily.
3. The cat has ______________ a mouse.
4. Betty has ______________ a cake for her grandmother.
5. The soldiers were ______________ the castle.
6. That big, friendly dog was ______________ my hand.
7. My older sister has ______________ me how to knit.
8. The horses were ______________ a heavy cart.
9. George was ______________ the paper carefully with a pair of scissors.
10. The clouds are ______________ the sun from view.
11. Mum was ______________ the soup with a big wooden spoon.
12. The children were ______________ a lot of questions.

E *Look at the pictures on this page. Then write a sentence on what each picture shows.*

1. ______________________

2. ______________________

3. ______________________

4. ______________________

5. ______________________

6. ______________________

Lesson

You now know **four important rules** for making **good sentences**.

1. *A good sentence must have a* ***beginning*** *and an* ***ending****. It must* ***make complete sense****.*
2. *A good sentence must have* ***all the words needed*** *but* ***no extra words****.*
3. *The words in a good sentence must be in the* ***right order****.*
4. *A good sentence must have* ***correct punctuation****. It must end with a* ***full stop****, a* ***question mark*** *or an* ***exclamation mark****.*

Here is the **fifth** rule.

5. *A good sentence must* ***finish in the right place****.*

Look at these sentences.

- I've lost my key it was in my pocket.
- John was eating a pear he likes pears.
- Mary was playing with her dolls she often plays with dolls.
- Simon slipped on the ice he hurt his knee.

These sentences have ***too much*** *in them. Each one is really* ***two*** *sentences. The two sentences need to be split.*

Now look at these pairs of sentences.

I've lost my key.
It was in my pocket.

John was eating a pear.
He likes pears.

Mary was playing with her dolls.
She often plays with dolls.

Simon slipped on the ice.
He hurt his knee.

*The sentences in each pair are **good** sentences. Each sentence ends in the **correct place**.*

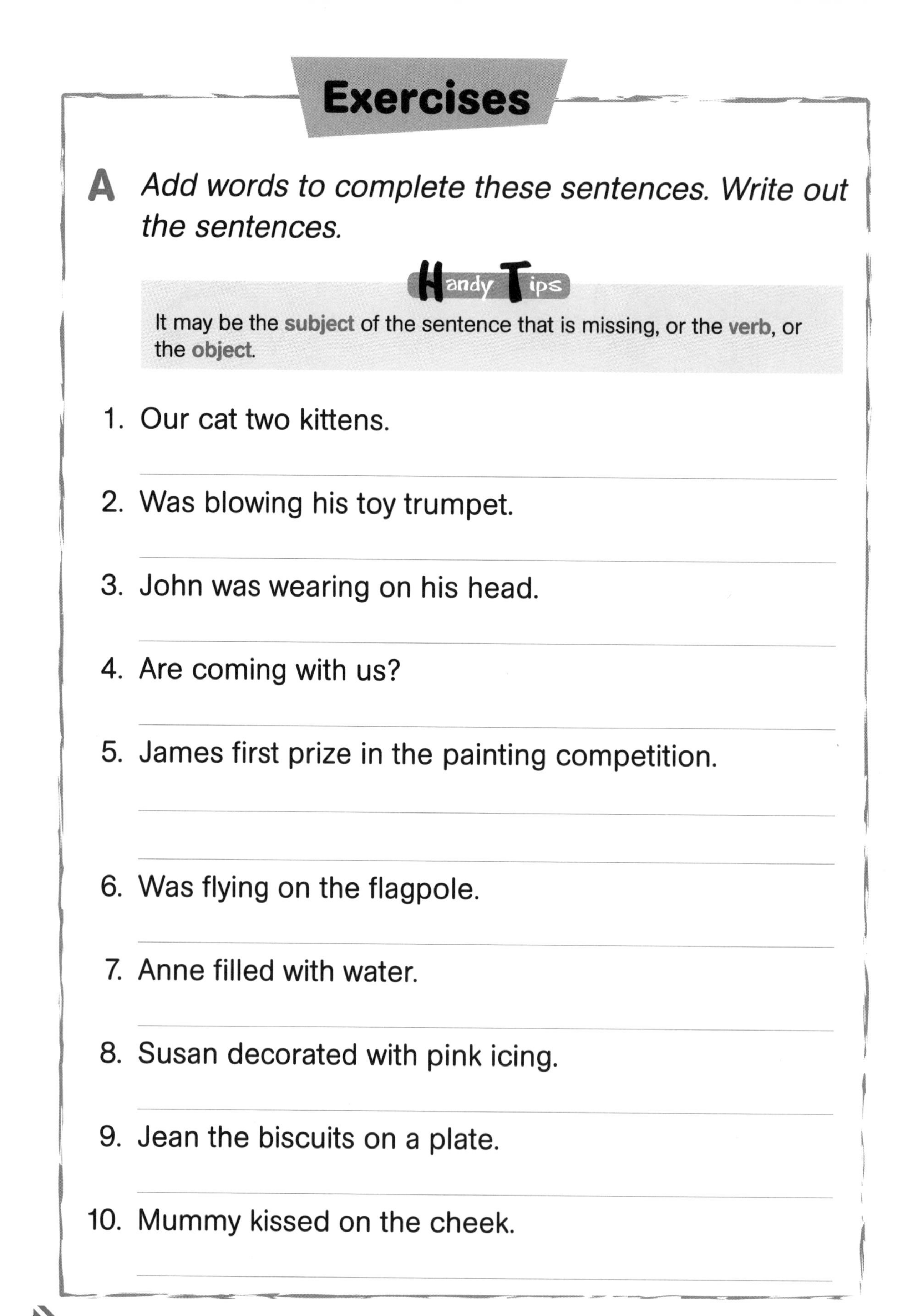

Exercises

A *Add words to complete these sentences. Write out the sentences.*

Handy Tips

It may be the **subject** of the sentence that is missing, or the **verb**, or the **object**.

1. Our cat two kittens.
2. Was blowing his toy trumpet.
3. John was wearing on his head.
4. Are coming with us?
5. James first prize in the painting competition.
6. Was flying on the flagpole.
7. Anne filled with water.
8. Susan decorated with pink icing.
9. Jean the biscuits on a plate.
10. Mummy kissed on the cheek.

B *Put the words in each group in the correct order to form a sentence.*

Handy Tips

Don't forget to begin each sentence with a **capital letter** and end the sentence with the correct **punctuation mark**.

1. would cup you a of like coffee

2. left i the umbrella my on bus

3. made this two you sentence have mistakes in

4. the tails monkeys long furry had

5. you other seen have my sock

6. your in my has dug dog a hole garden

7. about alien an did the story read you

8. likes in the jane choir singing

9. piece wants of another who cake

10. watch birthday peter received for a his

C *Find the mistakes in these sentences, and write out the sentences correctly.*

Handy Tips

To help you, the number of mistakes in each sentence is shown in brackets.

1. is raining again? (2)

2. John drawing picture of a castle. (2)

3. Simon and sally is going to the cinema. (2)

4. I has never seen anything like that before (2)

5. where are my clean shirt (3)

6. the dog picked up the shoe with its mouth (2)

7. Have you Seen my bike. (2)

8. The owls was hooting in the trees. (1)

9. when does the holidays start (3)

10. the teacher was writing on board. (2)

D *Make two sentences with each group of words. Write them out, putting in correct **punctuation marks** and **capital letters.***

EXAMPLE:

there are three baby birds in that nest the parents are feeding them

There are three baby birds in that **nest. The** parents are feeding **them.**

1. look out the books are going to fall

2. that's a lovely picture did you paint it yourself

3. my little brother has a stomach ache he ate too much ice cream last night

4. it's stopped raining the sun is shining

5. who's taken my pencil it was on my desk just now

6. do you see that cat what is it doing

7. don't swing on that rope it might break

8. our cat has two kittens our neighbour's cat has three

9. the children were very poor their clothes were old and torn

10. those shoes look very smart where did you buy them

11. tortoises have hard shells they move about very slowly

12. the soldiers were carrying guns they were guarding the castle

E *Rewrite this story, putting in* ***capital letters*** *and* ***punctuation marks*** *where they are needed.*

A brave dog

there was once a rich man who lived in a big house in the country the man had a baby son and a dog called Benny

one day the man had to go into the town he told Benny to guard the baby Benny lay down beside the baby's cot

an hour passed then a wolf jumped into the room through an open window

Benny got to his feet and fought with the wolf he killed the wolf after a long fight

after another hour the rich man returned he saw the dead wolf and guessed what had happened he was very happy he hugged his baby son and Benny

Lesson

A **pronoun** is a word that can be used **instead of a noun**.

*Common pronouns are **I, me, you, he, him, she, her, it, we, us, they** and **them**.*

When you **answer a question**, you often use a **pronoun** instead of a **noun**.

Let's look at some questions and answers.

"Where is **my coat**?"
"**It**'s on the peg over there."

"Why is **that dog** barking?"
"**It** doesn't like that man."

"What are **the boys** doing?"
"**They**'re playing tennis."

"Why is **that little girl** crying?"
"The dog frightened **her**."

*You should use **pronouns** instead of nouns when you are writing several sentences about the same person, animal or thing.*

Look at these groups of sentences.

There were **two birds** sitting in the tree. **They** were singing happily. **They** did not see a cat creeping up behind **them**.

Nancy and her mother were shopping. First **they** went into the supermarket to buy some fruit. Then **they** went into the shoe shop to buy a pair of sandals for Nancy.

The car rolled fast down the hill. First **it** swung round one corner. Next **it** rolled round another corner. Then **it** hit a tree. And finally **it** fell into the river.

Exercises

A *Draw circles round the **pronouns** in these sentences.*

1. Can you see me?
2. I am very busy at the moment.
3. Mummy was a little bit cross with us.
4. James rubbed his eyes. He was very sleepy.
5. She tried to climb in through the window. It was too small.
6. Have you lost your keys? Don't worry. We will soon find them.
7. Your mother will be pleased to see you. She has been very worried about you.
8. Tim turned round. There was a cow standing behind him. She was looking at him with enormous, brown eyes.
9. I used to have lovely flowers in my garden. Do you know where they went? The rabbits ate them!
10. Where is Sally? We are all looking for her.

B *Rewrite these sentences, replacing the underlined words with suitable* ***pronouns****.*

1. My brother is a very good painter. <u>My brother</u> has won many prizes for his paintings.

2. The twins had new bikes for their birthday. <u>The twins</u> were very pleased.

3. My little sister likes swimming. <u>My little sister</u> swims like a fish.

4. The boys ran as fast as <u>the boys</u> could, but <u>the boys</u> couldn't catch the balloon.

5. The dogs were in the garden. <u>The dogs</u> were chasing each other round and round.

6. This box is very heavy. Where shall I put <u>the box</u>?

7. My father was singing happily as my father washed the dishes.

8. The little girl was crying. The big dog had frightened the little girl.

9. The bird flew out of the tree. The bird landed on the roof.

10. I can't find my sports shoes. Where did you put my sports shoes?

11. My friends are going on holiday next week. My friends are going to Australia.

12. John is going to the cinema tonight. Can I go with John?

C *Rewrite these sentences, replacing the subjects and objects with* ***pronouns****.*

EXAMPLE:
John broke the branch.
He broke **it**.

1. Sally spilt the milk.

2. The mouse was eating the biscuits.

3. My cousins and I were building sandcastles on the beach.

4. The bull knocked the man over.

5. My grandfather is reading the newspaper.

6. John and Henry have found the keys.

7. Vicky always feeds her pet parrots.

8. How did Mary hurt her leg?

9. Where did Jan and Billy hide?

10. Mike hit the ball high into the air.

D *Answer the following questions, using pronouns for the subjects of the sentences. Start all your answers with* ***Yes****.*

EXAMPLES:
Does James like pizza?
Yes, he likes pizza.

Do you like pizza?
Yes, I like pizza.

Handy Tips

Your answers do not need to be true. (If you don't have any brothers or sisters or pets, you can pretend that you have.)

And be careful with the verbs!

1. Does your brother like his teacher?

___

2. Do your sisters like watching television?

___

3. Does your dog sleep in the kitchen?

___

4. Do you like snakes?

___

5. Is your father a teacher?

___

6. Does your mother shop at the local market every morning?

7. Do the boys have organ lessons every Saturday?

8. Does her uncle wear glasses?

9. Do you play the trumpet?

10. Do Jean and John like listening to music?

11. Does your school uniform need to be washed every day?

12. Do cats and dogs always fight?

13. Are you interested in stamp collecting?

14. Were you angry about anything yesterday?

15. Have you and your family been abroad for holidays?

E *Look at each picture. Then write **two** sentences on what the picture shows.*

*The first sentence should begin with **There is** or **There are**. The subject of the second sentence should be a **pronoun**.*

EXAMPLE:

There are two dogs in this picture. **They** are fighting.

1. ______________________________

____

____

____

2. ______________________________

____

____

____

3.

4.

5.

6.

UNIT 7 Making sentences more interesting

Lesson 1

An **adjective** is a word that **describes someone or something**.

Crocodiles have very **sharp** teeth.

The beach is very **crowded**.

We caught a **big** fish. We were very **happy**.

Santa Claus carried a **large**, **heavy** sack on his back.

Monkeys' tails are **long** and **furry**.

Lesson 2

Adverbs are words that **describe when** or **where** or **how** things happen.

Adverbs of time *say* ***when*** *things happen:*

- I saw something very strange **yesterday**.
- May I have a biscuit **now**?
- Come back **soon**.

Adverbs of place *say* ***where*** *people or things are or* ***where*** *they are going:*

- Should I put this chair **here**?
- No, put it **there**.
- The horses galloped **away**.

Adverbs of manner *describe* ***how*** *things happen:*

The dogs were barking **loudly**.

The children were playing **happily** in the garden.

The robber **quickly** ran away.

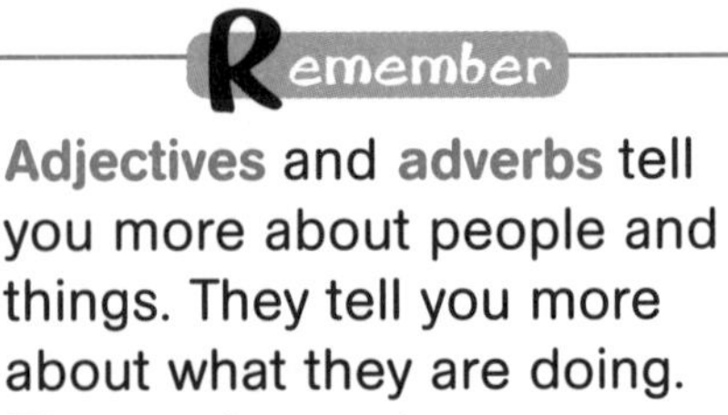

Remember

Adjectives and **adverbs** tell you more about people and things. They tell you more about what they are doing. **They make sentences more interesting.**

Exercises

A *Draw a circle round each adjective in these sentences.*

1. The boxes are empty.
2. The children are very excited.
3. Tortoises have hard shells.
4. The old lady was very kind to us.
5. There were muddy footprints all over the new carpet.
6. We were feeling very hungry after our long journey.
7. The clever clowns with pointed hats were balancing on big, red balls.
8. The tall trees made dark shadows on the high wall.
9. Dad broke the big, hard rock with a heavy hammer.
10. A strange noise was coming from the deserted house.

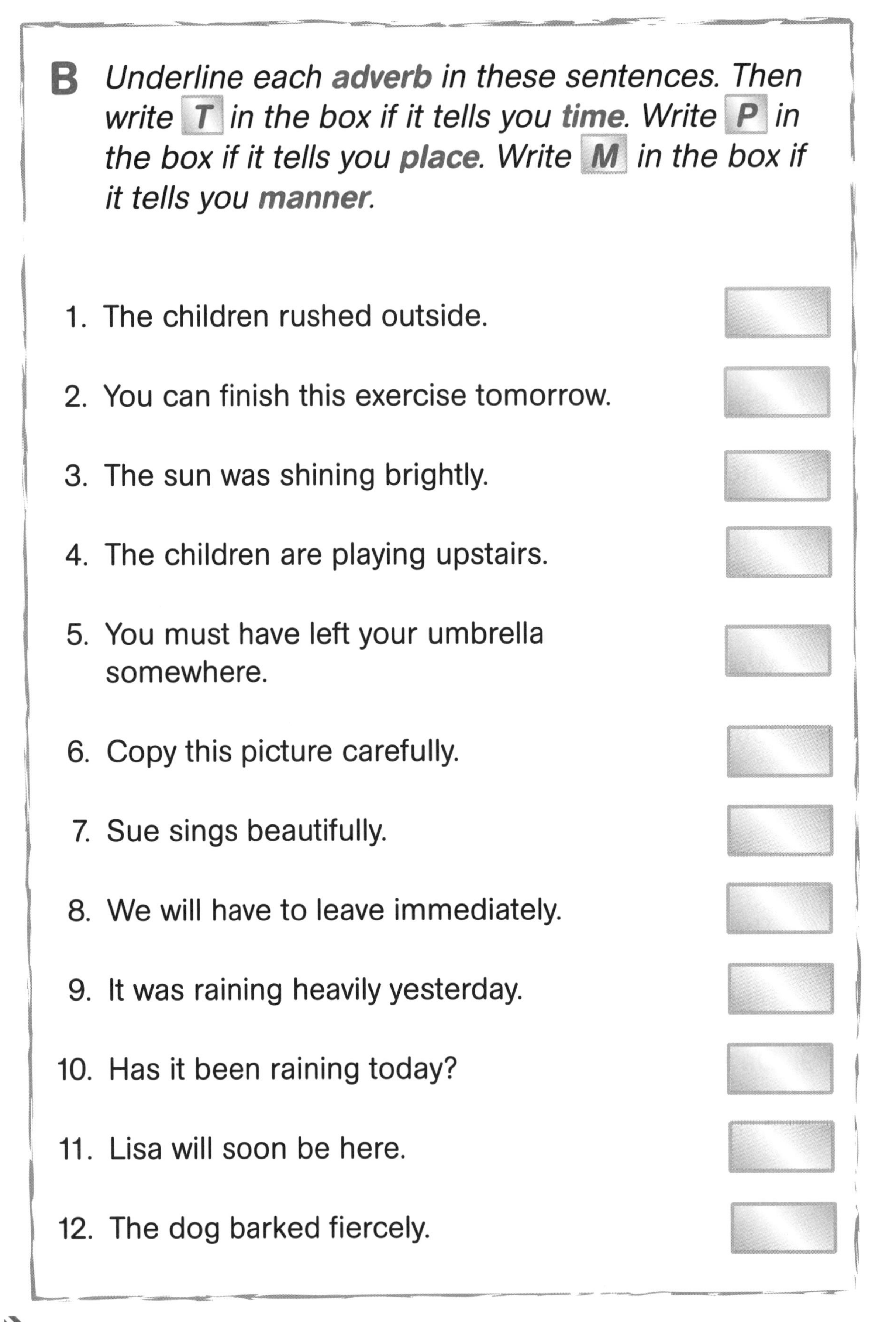

B *Underline each **adverb** in these sentences. Then write **T** in the box if it tells you **time**. Write **P** in the box if it tells you **place**. Write **M** in the box if it tells you **manner**.*

1. The children rushed outside.
2. You can finish this exercise tomorrow.
3. The sun was shining brightly.
4. The children are playing upstairs.
5. You must have left your umbrella somewhere.
6. Copy this picture carefully.
7. Sue sings beautifully.
8. We will have to leave immediately.
9. It was raining heavily yesterday.
10. Has it been raining today?
11. Lisa will soon be here.
12. The dog barked fiercely.

C *Complete these sentences with suitable adjectives.*

1. I live in a ________________ town.
2. This is a very ________________ book.
3. Leaves and grass are ________________.
4. Pandas have ________________ and ________________ fur.
5. We felt very ________________ after our trip to the zoo.
6. The teacher told the ________________ children to be ________________.
7. The water in the swimming pool is not very ________________.
8. The clowns were wearing ________________ clothes.
9. Ants are very ________________ insects.
10. A ________________, ________________ dog frightened us.
11. There were lots of ________________, ________________ flowers in the garden.
12. Witches wear ________________, ________________ hats and ________________, ________________ cloaks.

D *Complete each sentence with a suitable adverb of manner.*

1. The baby was playing ________________ on the floor.
2. The dogs barked ________________ at the strange man.
3. The old man walked ________________ along the road.
4. It rained ________________ all afternoon.
5. The cat crept ________________ through the bushes.
6. The boys were laughing ________________.
7. We all ran ________________ down the street.
8. The children on the bus were all singing ________________.
9. The old man shouted ________________ at the silly boys.
10. Sam held his mother's hand ________________.
11. Joe carried the jug of water ________________ into the dining room.
12. The soldiers fought ________________.

E *Read this story. Then write out the story, adding suitable adjectives and adverbs to make the story more interesting. Underline the adjectives and adverbs you use.*

The sun was shining. Birds were singing in the trees. On the grass under one tree, there was a squirrel. It had eyes, fur, paws and a tail. The squirrel sniffed at the leaves under the tree. It was

looking for nuts and berries to store in its hole in the tree trunk. The squirrel heard a noise. It stopped sniffing the leaves. It listened. Perhaps there was a fox nearby. Without finding out, the squirrel scampered back to its hole to hide.

UNIT 8 Adverb phrases

Lesson

Instead of adverbs, you can use **phrases** to describe **where** something is, **when** something happens or **how** something happens.

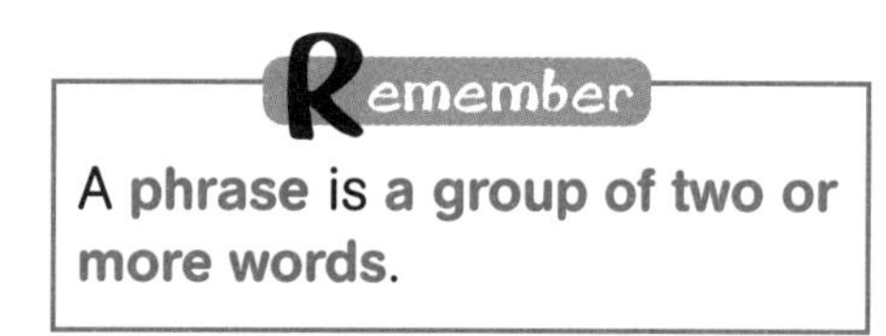

Remember

A **phrase is a group of two or more words.**

*Here are sentences with **phrases** that describe **where** someone or something is.*

The children are playing **on the beach**.

Mum is busy making a cake **in the kitchen**.

She hangs her coat **on a peg**.

My dad works **in a bank**.

The boys are standing **at the bus stop**.

*Here are sentences with **phrases** that describe **when** something happens.*

*Here are sentences with **phrases** that describe **how** something happens.*

The cars were all going **at great speed**.

The cow looked at him **with enormous eyes**.

Exercises

A *Underline the phrase in each sentence that describes **where** or **when** or **how** something happens. Write **where**, **when** or **how** in the box.*

1. The dog dropped the stick on the ground.
2. Can you come tomorrow afternoon?
3. The farmer walked across the field.
4. The little girl hid behind the chair.
5. There was a puddle of water on the floor.
6. At that very moment it started to rain.
7. The parcel landed with a thud.
8. Tea will be ready in five minutes.
9. The cat had a little bird in its mouth.
10. She was speaking in a very soft voice.
11. Frightened, the horse jumped over the fence.
12. Once upon a time there was a brave knight.

B *Complete each sentence with a suitable ending from the box.*

round the field	in the oven	in the teapot
in the cupboard	in the park	on the pond
in the refrigerator	on the sea	in its cot
in silver paper	in a vase	in the jungle

1. The boys were playing football ____________________.
2. Grandma put the cake ____________________.
3. The ducks were swimming ____________________.
4. Put your shoes ____________________.
5. Mum poured out the water ____________________.
6. The horses were galloping ____________________.
7. The nurse put the baby ____________________.
8. Shall I put these flowers ____________________?
9. We wrapped Pam's present ____________________.
10. Put the ice cream ____________________.
11. Boats were sailing ____________________.
12. Tigers live ____________________.

C *Replace the adverb in each sentence with a phrase from the box.*

EXAMPLE:
Tom shut the door noisily.
Tom shut the door **with a bang**.

all of a sudden	after that	by accident
in a quiet voice	in a loud voice	first of all
in a little while	in the garden	in the house
once upon a time	right away	this evening

1. Suddenly the door opened.

   ________________ the door opened.

2. The wizard began to sing loudly.

   The wizard began to sing ________________.

3. Go and play outside.

   Go and play ________________.

4. I accidentally broke the clock.

   I broke the clock ________________.

5. First we must wrap the parcel.

   ______________________ we must wrap the parcel.

6. We'll soon be at the beach.

   We'll be at the beach ______________________.

7. We're not allowed to play indoors.

   We're not allowed to play ______________________.

8. You can watch television tonight.

   You can watch television ______________________.

9. Sheila spoke to the kitten quietly.

   Sheila spoke to the kitten ______________________.

10. We will have to do our homework now.

    We will have to do our homework ______________________.

11. There was once a beautiful cat.

    ______________________ there was a beautiful cat.

12. What did the man do next?

    What did the man do ______________________?

D *Answer the questions in complete sentences.*

1. Do polar bears live in hot countries or in cold countries?

2. Can penguins swim in the sea?

3. Can penguins fly in the air?

4. Do octopuses live in the jungle or in the sea?

5. Do sheep and cows live on farms?

6. Do you eat supper in the morning?

7. What animals live in hutches?

8. How many wheels are there on a bicycle?

9. Do you see the sun at night?

10. Do rabbits live in kennels?

E *Write seven sentences describing what you see in the picture.*

1. ______________________________

2. ______________________________

3. ______________________________

4. ______________________________

5. ______________________________

6. ______________________________

7. ______________________________

UNIT 9 Joining sentences

Lesson

You can join sentences using the word **and**.

Look at these sentences:

- Tom plays the piano.
- May plays the violin.

*You can make these two sentences into one longer sentence using the word **and**:*

- Tom plays the piano **and** May plays the violin.

And is used to make **two short sentences** into **one longer sentence**.

*Let's look at more sentences with the word **and** in them.*

- Pam gave Simon a book **and** Simon gave Pam a box of crayons.
- Martin has blue eyes **and** his sister has brown eyes.
- Elephants are big **and** mice are small.

There is another way of joining sentences with **and**.

Look at these sentences:

- Tom plays football.
- Mike plays football.

You can make these two sentences into one sentence using the word ***and*** *in this way:*

- Tom **and** Mike play football.

You can join ***subjects*** *with* ***and****:*

- Lisa **and** Peter like singing.

You can join ***verbs*** *with* ***and****:*

- Lisa sings **and** dances beautifully.

You can join ***objects*** *with* ***and****:*

- We bought a jacket **and** a pair of shoes.

You can join ***adverbs*** *with* ***and****:*

- Joe walked slowly **and** carefully with the jug.

Exercises

A *Join the two sentences in each pair to make* ***one longer sentence*** *using the word* ***and****.*

Handy Tips

Be careful with the **capital letters** and the **full stops**.

1. Paul drank orange juice.
   Mary drank lemonade.

2. John has three sisters. Simon has two brothers.

3. I have an apple. Tom has a banana.

4. Kittens are baby cats. Puppies are baby dogs.

5. I like playing football. My sister likes playing tennis.

6. The boys were watching television. The girls were reading books.

7. Monkeys have long tails. Rabbits have short tails.

B *Make new sentences by joining the **subjects** of these pairs of sentences with **and**.*

1. Lemons are yellow. Bananas are yellow.

Handy Tips

Look carefully at your new sentences. You may have to make some other changes when you join the subjects.

2. Whales live in the sea. Sharks live in the sea.

3. Seals can swim. Penguins can swim.

4. Leaves are green. Grass is green.

5. Eagles are birds. Owls are birds.

6. Knives are used for cutting things. Scissors are used for cutting things.

7. Sugar is sweet. Honey is sweet.

8. Irene wore red shoes to the party. Mary wore red shoes to the party.

C *Make new sentences by joining the **objects** or the **adverbs** or **adverb phrases** of these pairs of sentences with **and**.*

1. William put the plates in the cupboard. William put the cups in the cupboard.

2. I ate a sandwich. I ate a chocolate biscuit.

3. Tommy read the instructions slowly. Tommy read the instructions carefully.

4. The old lady lost her keys. The old lady lost her purse.

5. We saw lions at the zoo. We saw tigers at the zoo.

6. The children ran out of the house. The children ran into the garden.

7. George washed his hands. George washed his face.

8. Sarah knitted a hat. Sarah knitted a pair of gloves.

D *Join the sentences with* ***and.***

Handy Tips

In this exercise, you have to decide which parts of the sentences can be joined by **and**.

1. Pandas are black and white. Panthers are black.

2. Pandas are black and white. Zebras are black and white.

3. There were sheep in the field. There were cows in the field.

4. There were cows in the field. There were cows in the farmyard.

5. We baked a cake. We baked some biscuits.

6. Hippopotamuses have big mouths. Elephants have long trunks.

7. Elephants have tusks. Elephants have long trunks.

8. John gave me a bar of chocolate. I gave John some sweets.

9. John gave Mary some bars of chocolate. John gave me some bars of chocolate.

10. Mary likes chocolate. I like chocolate.

11. There were two plates on the table. There was a cup on the table.

12. I washed the dishes after dinner last night. I dried the dishes too.

13. Lisa sings beautifully. She dances beautifully too.

14. The teacher thought of a story. He told his class the story with actions.

E *All the **and**'s are missing from this story. Rewrite the story, putting the word **and** in the places where it is needed.*

Last Saturday Mum said we were all going for a picnic on the beach. My sister Jenny I were very pleased. We like picnics.

Mum made some cheese tomato sandwiches. She wrapped the sandwiches put them some biscuits in a hamper. Jenny I packed cups plates in a carrier bag. We also packed some bottles of orange juice lemonade.

Dad put the bag the hamper in the boot of the car. He put buckets spades in the boot too. Mum Dad got into the front of the car Jenny I sat in the back. Then off we went.

Soon we were at the beach. We opened the boot took out the bag the hamper. We sat on the beach ate our picnic. Then Jenny I used the buckets spades to build a huge sandcastle.

But slowly steadily clouds covered the sky it started to rain. We all got in the car Dad drove us home.

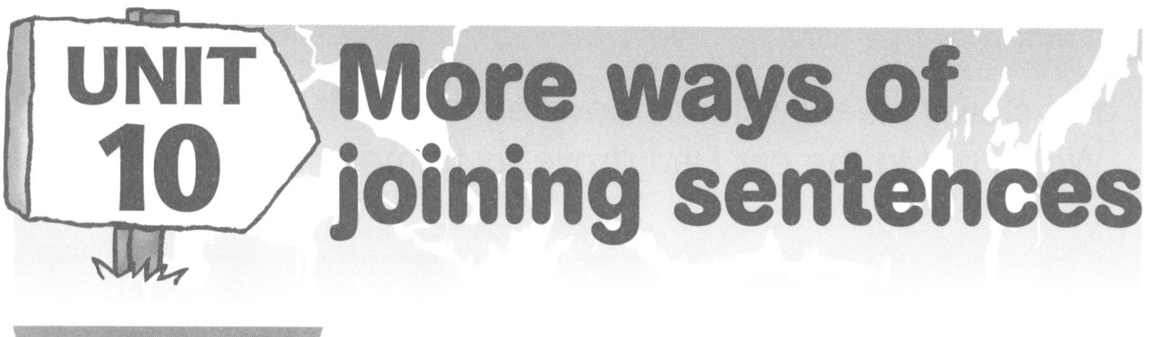

UNIT 10 More ways of joining sentences

Lesson

There are other words that you can use to **join short sentences together to make longer sentences**.

Some joining words help to say ***when*** *something happens.*

He laughed **as** he watched the clowns.

He polished his shoes **until** they shone.

Look both ways **before** you cross the road.

Our neighbours looked after our cat **while** we were on holiday.

*Some joining words help to say **why** something happens.*

The baby was crying **because** she was hungry.

I'll help you with these boxes **since** you have more to carry.

We caught an earlier bus **as** we didn't want to arrive late.

Take an umbrella **in case** it rains.

He tied a rope round the dog's neck **so that** it couldn't run away.

Language Help

Did you notice? **As** and **since** can be used to tell you **when** something happens. They can also be used to tell you **why** something happens.

Exercises

A *Write* **when** *in the box when the sentence tells you* ***when*** *something happens. Write* **why** *in the box when the sentence tells you* ***why*** *something happens.*

1. They laughed when they saw the dog chasing the stick.
2. I'll look after the baby while you go shopping.
3. The boys hid behind a tree so that no one would see them.
4. I ran away quickly because there was a bull in the field.
5. I'll take some chocolate with me in case I get hungry.
6. Stay in bed until you feel better.
7. We'll need to wash the mud off the car when we get home.
8. Tom smiled as he saw the door open.
9. Everyone was annoyed with him as he was making a lot of noise.
10. Wait at the shop until I get there.
11. I'll carry the bags since you're carrying the boxes.
12. We've been learning English since we started school.

B Read each sentence and complete the joining word that tells **when** something happens.

Handy Tips

There may be more than one correct answer.

1. He was whistling a______________ he walked along the road.
2. I'll see you w______________ I get home.
3. You can watch television a______________ you have finished your homework.
4. Wash your hands b______________ you eat.
5. Always brush your teeth a______________ you have eaten something.
6. Anne has been Nancy's best friend s______________ they both started school.
7. I like to listen to music w______________ I do my homework.
8. We closed the gate b______________ we let our dog out of the house.
9. Everyone cheered a______________ the soldiers marched past.
10. You can buy some popcorn w______________ we get to the beach.
11. I'll give Monty a bath a______________ I've taken him for a walk.
12. The children have grown a lot s______________ I saw them last year.

C *Read each sentence and complete the joining word that tells **why** something happens.*

1. Tom was late for school b______________ he stayed in bed too long.
2. Take some money with you i______________ you want to buy some sweets.
3. They ran home quickly a______________ it was nearly time for tea.
4. Speak loudly s______________ everyone can hear you.
5. We had to play indoors s______________ it was raining.
6. We closed the gate s______________ the cows could not get out of the pen.
7. The dog was howling b______________ it was lonely.
8. We'll take our swimming costumes with us i______________ we have time for swimming.
9. I'll post that letter for you s______________ I go past the post office on my way to school.
10. They didn't want to leave the party b______________ they were having fun.
11. We didn't eat the mushrooms a______________ they might be poisonous.
12. Grandma looked after the baby s______________ Mummy could have a rest.

D *Complete each sentence, providing a reason for the action described in the first part.*

1. James was late for school because the bus ______________________________.
2. Pam washed her hands because they ______________________________.
3. We had to be very quiet because the baby ______________________________.
4. We were happy because the news ______________________________.
5. We didn't go to the zoo because ______________________________.
6. The dog was barking because ______________________________.
7. We went to the swimming pool because ______________________________.
8. The rat ran into its hole because ______________________________.
9. I like school because ______________________________.
10. We gave Jean a present because ______________________________.

E *Look at each picture. Then complete the sentence, starting with the word **because** to describe what the picture shows.*

1. The girl is crying ______________________________

______________________________.

2. The children are going indoors

______________________________.

3. The cat is climbing the tree ______________________________

______________________________.

4. David is lying in bed ______________________________

______________________________.

5. The children are laughing ______________________________

______________________________.

6. Mary is happy ______________________________

______________________________.

Answers

Unit 1

A
1. Who 2. The pirates 3. The teacher
4. My shoes 5. The nurse 6. The ghost
7. The two boys 8. My dad and I
9. you 10. Jo and her brother
11. the kettle 12. We

B
1. must go 2. will see
3. are 4. found
5. were galloping 6. was wearing
7. is 8. has
9. have bought 10. Have ... washed
11. are ... carrying 12. have found
13. Is ... coming 14. Has ... replied

C *Here are possible answers.*
1. The dogs 2. Mummy 3. The old man
4. Grass 5. you 6. The wind
7. we 8. I 9. Grandma
10. The girls 11. Who 12. What/Who

D *Here are possible answers.*
1. buried 2. walking 3. went
4. eating 5. live 6. carrying
7. wearing 8. drink/lap 9. making
10. are 11. move/travel 12. walked/moved

E *Here are possible answers.*
1. The boy is looking at the aeroplane in a toy shop.
2. He decides to buy a model plane.
3. He takes out a piece of wrapping paper.
4. He is wrapping the model plane.
5. He is going to his friend's house with the present.
6. He gives the present to his friend.

Unit 2

A
1. S 2. C 3. S 4. C 5. C 6. S
7. S 8. S 9. C 10. C 11. C 12. C

B
1. We are going to write a story about a princess and a dragon.
2. Write about the princess being shut up in a dungeon.
3. What was the princess's name?
4. The princess's name was Flora.
5. What shall we call the dragon?
6. Call the dragon George.
7. Was the princess afraid of George?
8. George was a very gentle dragon.

C
1. Open the door!
2. Take this there.
3. Look at all those pretty flowers.
4. Please don't be so noisy.
5. Draw a picture of a bus.
6. Don't play football in the house!
7. Be careful with that sharp knife.
8. Stay away from that wasps' nest!

D **The glass slipper**

There was once a king. One day, one of his servants found something very surprising. "Show me this surprising thing," said the king. "Bring it to me."

It was a small, glass slipper. "Whose is this slipper?" asked the king. "Go into the town. Search everywhere. Find the owner of the slipper."

The servant went off into the town. He knocked on every door. "Are there any girls in this house?" asked the servant. "Bring them to me." To each girl the servant said, "Try on this slipper." But the girls' feet were always too big.

Finally the servant came to a house where he saw a young girl working in the kitchen. "Put this slipper on," said the king's servant. The girl tried it on. It fitted! The servant had found the right girl at last!

When the king met the girl, he fell in love with her. "Please marry me," he said. The girl happily agreed.

E *These are possible answers.*
1. Do not smoke.
2. Do not eat and drink here.
3. Do not fish in the pond.
4. Do not enter.
5. Do not cycle here.
6. Do not feed the monkeys.

Unit 3

A
1. ? 2. ! 3. ! 4. ? 5. ! 6. !
7. ! 8. ? 9. ! 10. ! 11. ? 12. ?

B
1. What a pity!
2. It's a mouse!
3. How lucky you are!
4. We've lost all our money!
5. You've won first prize!
6. What a great present this is!
7. The old tree has fallen down!
8. Someone has been eating my porridge!

C
1. How lucky we are!
2. What a good girl she is!
3. Those bad boys burst my balloon!
4. That dog bit me!
5. I've hurt my knee!
6. I'm frightened!
7. The computer isn't working!
8. The giant was taller than a tree!
9. You're just being silly!
10. That poor donkey!
11. He's broken my pencil!
12. What a tiny spider!

D *These are possible answers.*
1. How lovely! 2. What a pity!
3. What a mess you've made!
4. What a lucky girl I am!
5. How careless of me! 6. What a surprise!
7. What a clever boy! 8. How funny he looks!

E *These are possible exclamations.*
1. What a lovely cake! 2. Good dog!
3. Bad dog! 4. It's a mouse!
5. I'm lost! 6. I've won!

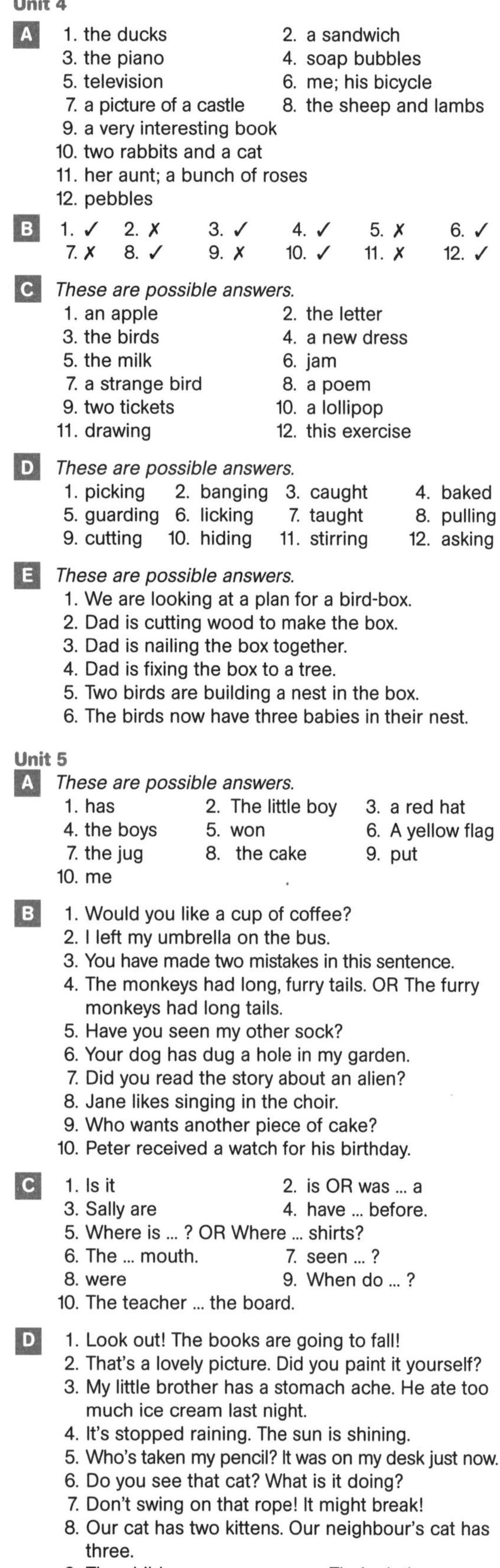

Unit 4

A
1. the ducks 2. a sandwich
3. the piano 4. soap bubbles
5. television 6. me; his bicycle
7. a picture of a castle 8. the sheep and lambs
9. a very interesting book
10. two rabbits and a cat
11. her aunt; a bunch of roses
12. pebbles

B
1. ✓ 2. ✗ 3. ✓ 4. ✓ 5. ✗ 6. ✓
7. ✗ 8. ✓ 9. ✗ 10. ✓ 11. ✗ 12. ✓

C *These are possible answers.*
1. an apple 2. the letter
3. the birds 4. a new dress
5. the milk 6. jam
7. a strange bird 8. a poem
9. two tickets 10. a lollipop
11. drawing 12. this exercise

D *These are possible answers.*
1. picking 2. banging 3. caught 4. baked
5. guarding 6. licking 7. taught 8. pulling
9. cutting 10. hiding 11. stirring 12. asking

E *These are possible answers.*
1. We are looking at a plan for a bird-box.
2. Dad is cutting wood to make the box.
3. Dad is nailing the box together.
4. Dad is fixing the box to a tree.
5. Two birds are building a nest in the box.
6. The birds now have three babies in their nest.

Unit 5

A *These are possible answers.*
1. has 2. The little boy 3. a red hat
4. the boys 5. won 6. A yellow flag
7. the jug 8. the cake 9. put
10. me

B
1. Would you like a cup of coffee?
2. I left my umbrella on the bus.
3. You have made two mistakes in this sentence.
4. The monkeys had long, furry tails. OR The furry monkeys had long tails.
5. Have you seen my other sock?
6. Your dog has dug a hole in my garden.
7. Did you read the story about an alien?
8. Jane likes singing in the choir.
9. Who wants another piece of cake?
10. Peter received a watch for his birthday.

C
1. Is it 2. is OR was ... a
3. Sally are 4. have ... before.
5. Where is ... ? OR Where ... shirts?
6. The ... mouth. 7. seen ... ?
8. were 9. When do ... ?
10. The teacher ... the board.

D
1. Look out! The books are going to fall!
2. That's a lovely picture. Did you paint it yourself?
3. My little brother has a stomach ache. He ate too much ice cream last night.
4. It's stopped raining. The sun is shining.
5. Who's taken my pencil? It was on my desk just now.
6. Do you see that cat? What is it doing?
7. Don't swing on that rope! It might break!
8. Our cat has two kittens. Our neighbour's cat has three.
9. The children were very poor. Their clothes were old and torn.
10. Those shoes look very smart. Where did you buy them?
11. Tortoises have hard shells. They move about very slowly.
12. The soldiers were carrying guns. They were guarding the castle.

E **A brave dog**

There was once a rich man who lived in a big house in the country. The man had a baby son and a dog called Benny. One day the man had to go into the town. He told Benny to guard the baby. Benny lay down beside the baby's cot. An hour passed. Then a wolf jumped into the room through an open window. Benny got to his feet and fought with the wolf. He killed the wolf after a long fight. After another hour the rich man returned. He saw the dead wolf and guessed what had happened. He was very happy. He hugged his baby son and Benny.

Unit 6

A
1. you ... me 2. I 3. us 4. He
5. She ... It 6. you ... We ... them
7. you ... She ... you 8. him ... She ... him
9. I ... you ... they ... them 10. We ... her

B
1. He 2. They 3. She
4. they ... they 5. They 6. it
7. he 8. her 9. It
10. them 11. They 12. him

C
1. She ... it 2. It ... them 3. We ... them
4. It ... him 5. He ... it 6. They ... them
7. She ... them 8. she ... it 9. they
10. He ... it

D
1. he likes 2. they like 3. it sleeps
4. I like 5. he is 6. she shops
7. they have 8. he wears 9. I play
10. they like 11. it needs 12. they fight
13. I am 14. I was ... something
15. we have

E *These are possible answers.*
1. There are two boys in this picture. They are fishing.
2. There is a puppy in this picture. It is chewing a slipper.
3. There are two animals in this picture. The tiger is chasing the deer.
4. There is a little girl in this picture. She is combing her doll's hair.
5. There are two girls in this picture. They are flying kites.
6. There are some people in this picture. They are watching fireworks.

Unit 7

A
1. empty 2. excited
3. hard 4. old ... kind
5. muddy ... new 6. hungry ... long
7. clever ... pointed ... big, red
8. tall ... dark ... high
9. big, hard ... heavy
10. strange ... deserted

B
1. outside P 2. tomorrow T
3. brightly M 4. upstairs P
5. somewhere P 6. carefully M
7. beautifully M 8. immediately T
9. heavily M; yesterday T
10. today T 11. soon T; here P
12. fiercely M

C *These are possible answers.*

1. big/small 2. interesting 3. green
4. black ... white 5. tired 6. noisy ... quiet
7. clean/cold 8. colourful 9. tiny
10. big, fierce 11. lovely, pink
12. pointed, black ... long, black

D *These are possible answers.*

1. happily 2. fiercely 3. slowly
4. heavily 5. quietly 6. loudly
7. quickly 8. beautifully 9. angrily
10. tightly 11. carefully 12. bravely

E *Here is one possible version of the story.*

The sun was shining brightly. Small, colourful birds were singing sweetly in the leafy trees. On the green grass under one big, old tree, there was a little squirrel. It had black eyes, brown fur, tiny paws and a long, bushy tail. The squirrel sniffed carefully at the dead leaves under the old tree. It was looking for nuts and juicy berries to store in its hole in the tree trunk. Suddenly the little squirrel heard a strange noise. It immediately stopped sniffing the leaves. It listened carefully. Perhaps there was a hungry fox nearby. Without finding out, the frightened squirrel scampered back to its hole to hide.

Unit 8

A

1. on the ground–where
2. tomorrow afternoon–when
3. across the field–where
4. behind the chair–where
5. on the floor–where
6. At that very moment–when
7. with a thud–how
8. in five minutes–when
9. in its mouth–where
10. in a very soft voice–how
11. over the fence–where
12. Once upon a time–when

B

1. in the park 2. in the oven
3. on the pond 4. in the cupboard
5. in the teapot 6. round the field
7. in its cot 8. in a vase
9. in silver paper
10. in the refrigerator 11. on the sea
12. in the jungle

C

1. All of a sudden the door opened.
2. The wizard began to sing in a loud voice.
3. Go and play in the garden.
4. I broke the clock by accident.
5. First of all, we must wrap the parcel.
6. We'll be at the beach in a little while.
7. We're not allowed to play in the house.
8. You can watch television this evening.
9. Sheila spoke to the kitten in a quiet voice.
10. We will have to do our homework right away.
11. Once upon a time there was a beautiful cat.
12. What did the man do after that?

D

1. Polar bears live in cold countries.
2. Yes, penguins can swim in the sea.
3. No, penguins can't fly in the air.
4. Octopuses live in the sea.
5. Yes, sheep and cows live on farms
6. No, we eat breakfast in the morning, and we eat supper in the evening.
7. Rabbits and hamsters live in hutches.
8. There are two wheels on a bicycle.
9. No, you see the moon and stars at night, and you see the sun during the day.
10. No, dogs live in kennels, and rabbits live in hutches.

E *These are possible answers.*

1. There is an elephant standing on a box.
2. There is a dog balancing on a ball.
3. There is a lady on a horse.
4. There is a dog jumping through a hoop.
5. There is a clown on a bicycle.
6. There is a lion in a cage.
7. There is a man putting his head in the lion's mouth.

Unit 9

A

1. Paul drank orange juice and Mary drank lemonade.
2. John has three sisters and Simon has two brothers.
3. I have an apple and Tom has a banana.
4. Kittens are baby cats and puppies are baby dogs.
5. I like playing football and my sister likes playing tennis.
6. The boys were watching television and the girls were reading books.
7. Monkeys have long tails and rabbits have short tails.

B

1. Lemons and bananas are yellow.
2. Whales and sharks live in the sea.
3. Seals and penguins can swim.
4. Leaves and grass are green.
5. Eagles and owls are birds.
6. Knives and scissors are used for cutting things.
7. Sugar and honey are sweet.
8. Irene and Mary wore red shoes to the party.

C

1. William put the plates and the cups in the cupboard.
2. I ate a sandwich and a chocolate biscuit.
3. Tommy read the instructions slowly and carefully.
4. The old lady lost her keys and her purse.
5. We saw lions and tigers at the zoo.
6. The children ran out of the house and into the garden.
7. George washed his hands and his face.
8. Sarah knitted a hat and a pair of gloves.

D

1. Pandas are black and white and panthers are black.
2. Pandas and zebras are black and white.
3. There were sheep and cows in the field.
4. There were cows in the field and in the farmyard.
5. We baked a cake and some biscuits.
6. Hippopotamuses have big mouths and elephants have long trunks.
7. Elephants have tusks and long trunks.
8. John gave me a bar of chocolate and I gave John some sweets.
9. John gave Mary and me some bars of chocolate.
10. Mary and I like chocolate.
11. There were two plates and a cup on the table.
12. I washed and dried the dishes after dinner last night.
13. Lisa sings and daces beautifully.
14. The teacher thought of a story and told his class the story with actions.

E Last Saturday Mum said we were all going for a picnic on the beach. My sister Jenny and I were very pleased. We like picnics.

Mum made some cheese and tomato sandwiches. She wrapped the sandwiches and put them and some biscuits in a hamper. Jenny and I packed cups and plates in a carrier bag. We also packed some bottles of orange juice and lemonade.

Dad put the bag and the hamper in the boot of the car. He put buckets and spades in the boot too. Mum and Dad got into the front of the car and Jenny and I sat in the back. Then off we went.

Soon we were at the beach. We opened the boot and took out the bag and the hamper. We sat on the beach and ate our picnic. Then Jenny and I used the buckets and spades to build a huge sandcastle.

But slowly and steadily clouds covered the sky and it started to rain. We all got in the car and Dad drove us home.

Unit 10

A

1. when	2. when	3. why	4. why
5. why	6. when	7. when	8. when
9. why	10. when	11. why	12. when

B

1. as	2. when	3. after	4. before
5. after	6. since	7. when OR while	
8. before	9. as	10. when	11. after
12. since			

C

1. because	2. in case	3. as	4. so that
5. since	6. so that	7. because	8. in case
9. since	10. because	11. as	12. so that

D *These are possible answers.*

1. James was late for school because the bus broke down on the way.
2. Pam washed her hands because they were dirty.
3. We had to be very quiet because the baby was sleeping.
4. We were happy because the news we heard was good.
5. We didn't go to the zoo because it was raining.
6. The dog was barking because it wanted to be let out of the house.
7. We went to the swimming pool because we wanted to swim.
8. The rat ran into its hole because a cat was chasing it.
9. I like school because my teacher is very kind.
10. We gave Jean a present because it was her birthday.

E *These are possible answers.*

1. The girl is crying because she has hurt her knee.
2. The children are going indoors because it is raining.
3. The cat is climbing the tree because the dog is chasing it.
4. David is lying in bed because he has a temperature.
5. The children are laughing because they are watching a funny clown.
6. Mary is happy because she is celebrating her birthday.